The Soldier That Wagged Her Tail

By

Dolores N. Morris

Published by KCM Publishing
A Division of KCM Digital Media, LLC

This story is a short biography of William Morris with a specific focus on his World War II experience. The dog's dialogue is a work of fiction and has been created to illustrate the relationship between William Morris and Trixie.

The Soldier That Wagged Her Tail by Dolores N. Morris

ISBN-13: 978-1-939961-23-5
ISBN-10: 1939961238

First Edition

Publisher: Michael Fabiano
KCM Publishing
www.kcmpublishing.com

KCM Publishing

a division of KCM Digital Media, LLC

Contents

Acknowledgements

THANK YOU: two of the most powerful words in the English language. Words that are never used enough and are always welcome to hear. This book was a long, emotional and challenging journey. It would never have been completed without the help, support, love and wisdom of the following recipients of my "thank you":

Thank you God. Nothing happens without you.

Thank you, my dear sister, Joan Morris, who was the first to say, "We have to tape dad's story so it's never lost."

Thank you, PS 19 Principal Mary Petrone and fifth grade master teacher, Christine Vigliotti, who allowed Dad the time to tell his story to their 5th grade classes for so many years. Because of your understanding and enthusiasm, hundreds of kids met a real hero.

Thank you, Fran Sears, producer and family friend, who worked tirelessly in filming Dad's "classes" that became the seeds for the website.

Thank you, Barbara Ulus, for your expertise and care in scanning the vintage photos.

Thank you, Lois De la Haba, my wonderful, faithful, and patient agent. You stuck with me, comforted me, supported me, and talked me back from the ledge so many times. You always believed in this story.

Thank you, Michael Fabiano, who patiently walked me through the publishing minefield with grace and cool.

Thank you, Marilyn Myers, my editor, who painstakingly guided me and made my words shine even brighter.

Thank you, to the many friends and family, who have supported this endeavor. Your encouragement was immeasurable.

Thank you, Mom for loving Dad and us, your family, and for being my most perfect example of stubborn strength.

Thank you, Dad, my hero. You are a great man, but an even greater father.

And, of course, thank you to a little brown mutt who stole his heart, saved his life, and brought him home.

Thank you Trixie!

Author's Note

For many years I participated in the Principal for a Day program at my elementary school alma mater. Over time, I observed the 5th grade students intently studying World War II as part of their history curriculum. This led me to work with the faculty to establish a special 3-week course with a real World War II hero, my father William A. Morris.

Mr. Morris regaled the spellbound students, over 100 each year, with his story. At the end of his "class" the students created books, poems, and even songs about what they'd learned, and they dedicated their graduation to him.

Based on the overwhelming reaction to this real hero's story, I decided along with my family that our father's story needed to be published. We want the world to know and understand this important piece of history on many levels.

Thus, *The Soldier that Wagged Her Tail* was born. The book captures all the stories he told the students each year and also integrates the history of Trixie.

Trixie is this little terrier mutt Dad found in England just before D-Day and Trixie stayed with him throughout the war...from Omaha Beach to the Battle of the Bulge. Trixie became a trusted companion and a way for my Father and the men he served with to get through tough situations.

The dog's dialogue included is the fictitious part of the story. However, it brings context because the stories are real and the war was torturous.

My Dad's story is part of the African American experience, the success of the WWII allies and an example of unstoppable human perseverance.

I wonder if Dad didn't find Trixie, would he be here today. Would I be here? We owe a lot to Trixie and I hope you enjoy the creativity in how the story is told.

Dolores N. Morris

The Soldier That Wagged Her Tail

Chapter One
War on the Horizon

1944

We're at war; there's no doubt about it. I've been seasick for about three weeks and I'm not alone in giving my lunch back to the sea. The Atlantic is not a thing you want to play with. She is deep and very rough. She can tear up large ships in no time at all if she has a mind to. There I was, on a ship surrounded by thirty or forty other troop ships, battle ships, gun ships, submarines, about a thousand ships in all. There are hundreds of us on board, and so many ships are carrying hundreds more. We're in the middle of the Atlantic—going into battle very soon. It's on all of our minds. Are we sailing to our deaths? Where are we going? What the hell is a young black man from Staten Island, New York, doing here?

Staten Island and Harlem 1938

I was the youngest in my family—a very close family. I pretty much stayed close to home. One night on the radio, I heard there was going to be a draft next year. It was 1938. They were getting ready to pass a law saying all seventeen- and eighteen-year-olds would have to serve one year of military service. I didn't want to be drafted. I wanted to join with my buddies. We wanted to join before it became a law. So, me, Sam Brown, and Archie Bomar headed up to Harlem to join the famous all black unit—the 369th. The Harlem Hellfighters is a famous unit from WWI. I never told my father, even though we were very close. I never told anyone—I just went. We got to the armory on 5th and 142nd street around noon. The crowd was huge. There were hundreds of young black men wanting to join the US Army. We couldn't even get close to the front door that day, so we went home and vowed to return the next day.

The next day we went back to the armory—early in the morning this time—and there was still a huge crowd. The three of us were shoved and pushed and eventually found ourselves at the front door of the armory. When the door opened, we were the first ones in. My friends and I got separated once we were inside. They put us in different rooms to take written tests and physical exams, and in a short while, I found out I'd passed. Then the official papers were stamped and I was told to wait in a huge auditorium. It seemed like hours, but finally I saw my buddies, Sam and Archie. They didn't look happy. They didn't make it. Sam had flat feet and Archie was too short, so I would be going into the army alone.

I adjusted to that fact right away. It sank in that I'd have to get used to making new buddies. My life was about to make a big change.

I was told to go home and come back in three days. I went home, and at family dinner that night, I announced that I had joined the army. After a bit of shocked silence, my father asked if this was really what I wanted. I replied a firm yes, but it was kind of a sad occasion, in a way. My dad was very sick, and we had a huge moving business to run. I should have been there to help run it and that concerned me. I wondered if I'd let them down. If it was on their minds, no one said anything about that. We all came together and prayed. All my brothers and sisters wished me well. I hugged my Dad and Mom for a very long time that night.

When I went back to the armory, I had to take more tests and then I was sent home again for three or four more days. However, the next time was going to be different. The army told me to return wearing my worst clothes because those clothes would be thrown out. I was told say my goodbyes to family and friends.

When I returned, the army issued me a uniform. Well, they really just threw one at me. The pants were three sizes too big, the shirt two sizes too small, and the helmet couldn't fit my head. I looked like a clown, but all of us did. We stayed in the armory for about five hours, and then we were lined up outside.

Then we marched, 1,300 of us in the 369th Harlem Hellfighters. I was trying to hold my pants up. I couldn't breathe in my tight shirt, and all the while, I was holding on to my pea-sized helmet and carrying a duffle on my back. I must have looked ridiculous, but I was proud and a little scared. We marched to the station to get on a train for an uncomfortable ride that took all day and all night. I woke up to the sound of sergeants shouting, telling us to get off the train, and we did. We were surrounded by several feet of snow. The cold was brutal, and I hate the cold. The snow was up to my thighs.

I innocently piped up, "Why worry? Tomorrow we will get a snow day." I can still hear the laughter.

"No snow days here son."

We were called "yard birds" back then; we were so new and so dumb.

We marched again, a mile or so to the barracks, Fort Ontario, Oswego, New York.

Five miles from Canada, this was the army.

Basic training was not easy. I wondered, man, what did I get myself into? Waking up at 6 a.m., marching, drills, learning to shoot guns, more marching, five-mile hikes, sleeping outside in the rain, marching in the rain...I really got sick of marching.

Basic training at Fort Ontario took eleven months, the longest eleven months of my life.

After basic training, I was transferred to Camp Edwards in Massachusetts. It just seemed like I couldn't get away from cold weather, but I was a little closer to home. In Camp Edwards, I was part of the Coast Artillery Antiaircraft unit. We were trained to shoot these huge guns that were used for shooting down enemy aircraft. Thankfully, nothing ever attacked us.

When Pearl Harbor happened, I was sent there as a part of the 369th Harlem Hellfighters.

After my stint in Hawaii, which was about a year, I was made a sergeant—150 of us from the 369th got promoted.

I was then sent back to the mainland to Camp Stewart, Georgia, as part of a new unit, the 4251st Quartermaster Truck Company.

We trained troops that were then transferred overseas, but they forgot to transfer us. Finally our group, the 150 black sergeants, got the call to go. You couldn't guess where we went first. Staten Island—yes, my home town— to Pouch Terminal, so the ship could load up for our trip overseas. Women were working the forklifts and the pier was loaded with people and equipment. I could see folks walking on the street. My family didn't live far from there, but I couldn't call or leave the ship. This was my last glimpse of home, of America, for a long time. I was sad, broken hearted; I had a case of the blues. Then I said to myself, "Snap out of it. You're in the army now." And I felt better.

One of the William A. Morris moving company trucks circa 1950.

Susie E. DeHart Morris on the steps on 88 Barker Street
Staten Island, New York.

William A. Morris Sr. on the steps of 88 Barker Street, Staten Island, NY.

Chapter Two
England's at War

England 1944

I miss my family. I miss Mom and the litter—my brother and sisters. I haven't seen anyone in so long. The air is quiet now. Sometimes it gets really loud, so I hide. Mom taught me that, and the soldier helped me learn not to be afraid. Me and my brother used to play with the soldiers. One taught me tricks. A nice man fed me. He had dark skin, the color of my brother's fur. He had a nice face. He smiled a lot. I liked those soldiers, even though Mom didn't trust "two legs."

One day, the big noises and the machines seemed to get closer and closer. And then the next day, the soldiers started leaving. My friend knelt down close to my face and said, "I can't take you, girl. Be good. Be safe." He had tears in his eyes. Then he patted me on the head and walked away with the others.

I tried following them, but I couldn't keep up. I got tired and found a place to sleep. When I woke up, there was no sign of them. I was alone. I was lost. No family...no mama...no litter.

So I just kept moving

Chapter Three
The Meeting

We sailed out into the Atlantic Ocean, and soon we were surrounded by hundreds of other ships, all kinds of ships: aircraft carriers, submarines, battleships, troop transport ships like ours, aircraft carriers; it was too incredible to describe. We had no idea where we were going, but seeing all of this, all the ships, I knew "it" was going to be big, whatever "it" was. Things were pretty quiet until the navy ships started to test their guns. Boy oh boy, what a sight and what a sound. God bless our navy.

Corporal Johnson found me in the mess hall.

"We're docking in about an hour, Sarge. I can't wait to get off this tub."

"Me too." Yea all of us can't wait to get on land—but for what?

I got out on deck—the beach appeared out of the fog. So, that's England. I wished Norcie could see this.

Norcie's my wife. Yea, I forgot. I'm a married man now. I married my childhood sweetheart. We really hadn't planned on getting married so fast. We thought we'd have all the time in the world to plan a big wedding. I had eight siblings and Norcie was one of ten. We talked about having a big wedding at the farm in Virginia, that's where she's from. Great food, music, family, and friends, but the war came. Pearl Harbor came.

Norcie and I got married on a two-day pass after I was told I'd be shipping out. I remembered her beautiful face... scared, but trying not to let me see how scared she was. I left her. I had no choice. I was married and I was going to war.

The docking was fast—the grey boredom of our weeks at sea changed instantly.

Thousands of hands and feet were moving in from different directions.

The port was Southampton. Never heard of it, but in those last five years since I'd been in, every place I'd been sent I had never heard of before....Buzzards Bay, Pearl Harbor, Camp Stewart, next Southampton, England.

Finally I was down the gangplank—next I was standing around in this grey, desolate place. Bombed out buildings were all around—stillness, ominous stillness—except for the noise we were making. There were no birds, no flies, no bees—only the jeeps, trucks, food, guns, and soldiers. We wobbled around on our sea legs for a bit and laughed at each other.

We kept ourselves busy doing exercises, stretching, talking, trying to figure out what was awaiting us, yet not trying to think of how bad it might be. Then, I thought I heard a dog barking.

The field where we waited was huge, crowded with soldiers—over ten thousand.

I found my unit just a bit north of all the rest. We were near our trucks and equipment, but we couldn't drive away yet; they had to be loaded. We waited here for our orders. Cpl. Robert Johnson—always smiling—was at our jeep. We were all excited to be on land, but behind the smiles, beyond the laughter of very young men, joking with each other was the fear—what were we doing here?

I smell water. I keep moving toward that smell, toward the water. Maybe my soldiers will be there. There's nothing but old buildings all around. They look like a big rock hit them. I think they call it a bomb. I can see the water and a lot of machines, big floating things on the water. Soldiers everywhere, so many, I can see some dark ones. Maybe my friend is there.

I'm going to get closer. They don't even look at me. These soldiers are different colors. Some are pale, almost white, like my baby sister's fur. A few almost step on me. I have to be careful. I'm not really afraid. I feel something strange, like someone I know is nearby. Maybe my friend.

No one looks familiar. I keep moving through this crowd. A few yards away, I see a group of dark ones. They look like my friends, but no, it's not them. I get closer. I hear one of them talking. His voice sounds so familiar; he sounds good and safe. Something is making me get closer to him, I don't know why. I need to make him see me.

"Hello, Hello...Look at me...Play with me."

"Take me with you. I'm a good pup."

There are so many of these dark ones. They are all so young. Mom called them human pups. I like this one, this guy talking and smiling with the others. A few of the others are saying, "Look at this dog. Where did she come from?"

I'm trying to get his attention. He looks so much like my friend. Maybe they were from the same litter. He seems to be in charge; the other soldiers listen to him.

"Hello, Hello." *He smiles at me. Maybe he wants to play.*

We've been standing around here for about two days, passing the time. I must be really tired or something. I hear barking again. Yes, that's a dog barking. What's a dog doing here? The guys are smiling and pointing—yup it's a dog, a brown young dog—maybe two years old, terrier mutt, but what a face. So he... no, it's a she. She's barking at me. What the...? She just dropped a rock on my boot.

"She wants to play, Sarge. She wants you to play."

I don't want to reach down there—she might bite. Another soldier picks up the rock and throws it. She gets the rock but barks at me.

Now some of the guys have gathered around. The look on their faces is like Christmas, young boys finding a puppy under the tree. But it's not Christmas...it's June, in England, and we're in a war.

I threw the little rock, and darn if that pup didn't bring it back to my foot. We played for a while; I gave her some water poured from my canteen into my helmet. She was so smart.

Before our game could resume, we got the word. "Attention. Move 'em out."

I hear them call him Sarge...what kind of name is that? It doesn't matter...I like him. I want him to like me. I need him to like me. He's so smart and good at the game. I love fetching anything, even rocks. The other soldiers are laughing as they watch us. This feels so right. This Sarge gives me some water. "Oh, thank you."

I want to play some more, but suddenly the laughing stops. It looks like they are getting ready to leave.

"No, NO...don't leave me...not again. Please take me with you. Please."

❈

No more time for play—the corporal was already in our jeep—our orders were to drive to an area near the English Channel. I guess this was it. But the dog, the dog was by my jeep, barking.

"She wants to go with us, Sarge. She wants to jump in the jeep."

"Come on, girl."

And she jumped in the back of the jeep like she owned it.

I swear she was smiling.

She barked again, as if to say, "Let's go, guys." I gave her a pat.

Well, we've got a new recruit, Johnson...what do we call her?

As we drive, the corporal and I try out different names... Lady? Duchess? The pup says nothing.

"How about Trixie? You like that name, girl? Trixie…"

She barks twice. Corporal Johnson almost falls from the jeep laughing.

"Oh, thank you." They didn't leave me. I'm not alone any more. This Sarge and Johnson really like me. But they keep calling me strange names. Mama told me human pups will do that. Wait, what did Sarge just say? Yes, that's it. That's my name. I'm Trixie. I'm a soldier, and I'm a dog.

My bride, Norcie Allen Morris, 1944.

Chapter Four
June 6, 1944

I liked driving—have always liked driving. I grew up around trucks and couldn't wait to learn to drive one. My father taught me to drive when I was very young. Yes, I loved driving, but this was different. This was driving in war. I didn't want to think about it. We drove for miles and miles; we didn't talk much. Corporal Johnson just looked around, not much scenery: burned and bombed out buildings, rubble. We drove all day and all night. When we stopped, we slept where we fell, Trixie right beside me.

I like riding in this thing, this "jeep." Bill, that's his name. Bill Morris. He's a good driver, and the man with him is Corporal Johnson, Robert Johnson. I like him too, but Bill belongs to me. I just knew it as soon as I saw him. I don't know where we're going. There are a lot of soldiers with us, a lot of jeeps and trucks. I'm getting a little tired and hungry. It's getting dark. When are we stopping?

We were near another beach. I couldn't see it, but the word was that the English Channel was just beyond those trees. Something big was going to happen very soon. I could feel it. My men were ready. Sixteen trucks loaded and ready for whatever this was. Trixie is very calm. I wonder who trained her. She even likes C rations.

I kept telling myself to remain calm. I had so much training, hard training.

All that marching: drills, obstacle courses, climbing ten-foot walls, rope ladders, crawling in the mud with bullets screaming over our heads, crawling under barbed wire. Marching, inspections, and shaking when we encountered our captain, Capt. Jessie W. Pollins. I'll never forget him. He was built like Goliath, with a voice to match.

We trained in every kind of weather, rising at 6 a.m. and falling out (literally) at 6 p.m. Tests, gun training, night training, orders, orders, and more orders. We never questioned. This was the army.

I was calm—I think the pup did that for me; she certainly helped. When she looked at me, there was no fear in her eyes. She put her head in my lap, and it felt as if we were back home somewhere in my folks' yard—not at a beach somewhere in England, getting ready for battle.

I knew she heard my silent prayer. The prayer I said every night, "Dear God, don't let me get killed over here where no one knows me, and don't let me become a prisoner of war with this vicious army. Amen."

Bill is quiet. He is praying. I know what that is. My mama told me some humans pray. It makes them calm and strong. I wouldn't want to be anywhere else but here with my Bill, but I can smell something else. Fear, I smell fear and death.

I learned that smell. I hear a big noise, like thunder and then like a hundred thunders. I know that sound. It's not good.

The noise was so close. The bombs were very close. It's starting. This is it. We'll be in the battle soon. Later, I'll find out that this was the largest invasion force in human history. I hoped to God that no one would ever see anything like this again, but what about Trixie? "Someone bring me some rope—someone bring me some clothesline." Trixie was going into battle with me—I had to keep her safe.

"First group is going in. Move out."

The first sergeant turned to me, "You boys are going next." Yes, we boys—we're going next—to a beach we never heard of, to perhaps die in its sand, for a country that still called us men "boys." The battle had been raging all night. It was early morning, our second day near the Channel. Words came down. We were next, and just like that, a long rope clothesline appeared.

Everyone is running around—some are leaving and going toward those trees. I could smell water nearby. Bill and the other dark men are going toward trucks that were parked by the trees. When Bill gets in, I do too. I'm never leaving him—he knows that now. He wraps some rope around me. He says it's a "harness." He said it will keep me safe. I wasn't worried.

Trixie wasn't even nervous—she was just excited. She let me put the rope on her like it was a normal thing. I was ready. Now I knew why we'd trained like we did at Camp Stewart, Georgia. We drove those trucks all day in mud and sand. We drove up mountains over rocks, learned to dodge boulders and drive in water. I'd trained my men on how to put this special grease on the engines. Every day, for two or three hours, we'd grease every part of those engines. Then we'd drive the trucks into a lake, to some flags in the water, until the water was up to our knees, then up to our waist, then up to our necks—the trucks never stalled. We never asked why. You didn't ask why in the army, but now I know why.

We could hear the battle going on all day. I wonder what happened with that first group. It couldn't be good. I prayed for them. I don't remember if I slept or ate.

"Good luck, Sarge. Good luck. See you at the top."

Then Bill's truck goes first. He drove down to the beach. I could see the bombs, the war on the other shore. We were going into that. He drove the truck into this big dumpster. It was a very big box, and about fifty boxes like ours were lined up on this beach. They called them LSTs (Landing Ship, Tanks), but to me they were just giant heavy boxes. There were four trucks in this thing—Bill in front. There was a door right in front of us. I heard the back door slam closed. I looked at Bill.

"Here we go, girl. Here we go."

Chapter Five
Omaha Beach: D-Day 2

I remembered it was about noon. I was in the English Channel—in this big steel box floating into war. We were about twenty-five miles away, but the noise was deafening. Bullets were bouncing off the sides of this thing. I wondered, what will happen when that door comes down? Trixie was wondering that, too. Her paws were on the dashboard. Thank God I had her in this homemade harness. It's high tide and the water is rough—I could feel it, even in this big tub.

The noise got louder. We're almost there. My hands are sweating. I pray my prayer and pat Trixie.

I knew we were close. It felt like bombs were right outside the door. I heard screams then, too. Screams I never want to hear again.

I have never been seasick. Thank goodness. I can smell death all around us—I think Bill can, too. But he's calm. We prayed together. I can hear screaming and I can smell blood—a lot of blood. But I'm not afraid.

�֍

I waited for the signal. The red light came on; I started my engine. Trixie's front paws rested on the dashboard. The wait seemed like hours, but in seconds the gang plank door slammed down into the water and the Channel rushed in. It was red. It was red with blood.

Oh my God. What I saw is not something any human should ever see. The bloody water, the soldiers' bodies, the parts of their bodies, men were blown apart right in front of us. Oh my God. My God. But I had to focus.

The light was finally green—my foot found the accelerator. Water was up to my chest. I had to keep pushing on the accelerator. The truck floated out into the channel. Trixie had disappeared—I couldn't look for her then. There she was. Jesus, keep us safe. I glanced at Trixie; she was floating, but was still looking forward at the horror in front of her. My foot was pressed down to the floor. Finally, we stopped floating; the wheels grabbed hold of the sand. We're out of the LST—we were going toward the beach. This is Normandy, Omaha Beach.

The water is cold. I've never seen water like this or heard sounds like this. The water is full of blood and bodies. The bullets are hitting the water near us. Bill told me to stay calm. There is no window in our truck, no doors. The water is coming in so fast. I'm floating.

Bullets are whizzing by us. Some hit the truck. I'm bounced all over the place. I get knocked out of the truck. The rope keeps me from floating away. I swim back into the truck. I can't see where we're going, but Bill keeps driving. A soldier runs next to our truck, screaming. I saw his arm blown off into the air. Bombs and bullets are all around. Bill keeps driving. Bill has a strap around his waist. It barely holds him in. I look back. More soldiers are running out of the big boxes onto the beach. All around us were soldiers, young men running into death, blown apart on the sand, struck down before they had a chance to fire.

One of the guys that patted my head before we left fell screaming. We can't stop.

"Keyboard" is down. Oh God. I saw the kitchen truck blow up into dust. God help them. Where were my trucks? I wanted to stop for these soldiers—badly wounded, calling for medics—but my orders were strict. I could not help anyone. I had to get this truck to the top of the hill. Orders said this would take fifteen minutes. It had already been three hours. These Germans were dug in good. Oh my God, the bodies. Blacks and whites: there is no segregation here. Every color was on that beach, every color was fighting for our country.

So many dead, so many dying all around us. Why do humans do this to each other? We don't. Our truck keeps dodging bullets and bombs. Now big rocks are coming down from the top. We move around them, and we barely miss some of them. Bill can sure drive. If one of those had hit us, well, it would be over.

I prayed so hard. I prayed all day. There was no time to cry. Just keep driving. I would never forget this; men disappearing right in front of my eyes, arms and legs blown off and scattered on the beach. Screams, moans—so much blood.

I could get a bit up the hill, then an explosion or boulder forced me back. There was no road, no planned path to follow. We were on our own. I tried everything I could think of, everything I learned in training. Now I knew why they had made us do all that stuff again and again. I twisted, I turned, still watching our boys getting slaughtered—hearing their cries, seeing the horror. But I had to keep driving, just keep driving, turning, and maneuvering around the holes, the explosions, the rocks, the bullets. Trixie saw everything. She wasn't barking or whimpering. She was a witness to this day, a witness to this sacrifice for freedom.

I drove all day, all night, and I drove all the next day. We never left the truck. We saw more death than any human should ever see. It was late afternoon—about 4 p.m. We had climbed the hundred-foot chalk cliff. We got to the top. We made it off the beach.

Chapter Six
Top of the Hill

All of us made it. When Trixie and I got there, we were greeted by some of the men. About an hour later, the last truck got up the hill. All sixteen trucks, my entire unit, made it to the top. It was a miracle. There was Corporal Johnson. At the last minute, he had to drive one of the trucks—it was the first time he wasn't by my side. He made it. We greeted each other holding back tears, hugging. Why had God spared us? It hadn't occurred to me until we made it. Thank God, thank God. After almost two days of no sleep and no food—we weren't sure what to do first—collapse or eat. We ate and food never tasted so good. Yes, it was cold and tasteless, but after all we'd just been through, it tasted like a meal from a five-star restaurant.

And being with my guys never felt so good. We relaxed, at last, and talked.

I saw Corporal Johnson. Then the one he called "Stick" and then Private. Edwards—Bill is so happy. They're all happy hugging...I am too. Everyone is tired, exhausted, and hungry...but I can hear their prayers. "Bless you, God." They are all so thankful.

✗

The battle was still going on down on the beach. Our boys were still dying.

But there were about two or three hundred up here with us that made it. We were in shock. What kind of war did we just survive? And why were we spared? No time to let that sink in. It was D-Day 3...and there was a lot to do.

I told the men to finish their C rations while Trixie and I headed to headquarters for our orders.

No more clothes line harness. One of the guys threw me some C-ration scraps. Boy, was I hungry. No food for two days. There were no hot meals yet. Bill said he'd feed me a very good meal, very soon. "Just hold on a bit longer, girl—OK?"

The first sergeant told me to have the men check their trucks, check the gear. They'd just gone through a rough two days—that's an understatement. No leave, no rest. The headquarters tent in camp hadn't even been set up yet. Everyone had the look of shock and gratitude on their faces. We were at war. We had just come through one of the worst and most important battles of the war, and yet not one of the white officers, not one captain or lieutenant came to pay respects, greet us, or simply acknowledge our existence. By now, we were used to it.

We had a lot to do. No time for sleep, a good meal, a letter home. My orders were to get the trucks ready to pick up supplies at a depot twenty-five or thirty miles away. All the trucks in our unit were to bring supplies to General Patton's tank corps. I got some directions and got ready to get in the truck, again. It was a tough grind. I gave the orders to my men, and all they did was put a smile on their faces and said, "Well, here we go again."

They were a great bunch of fellas. I never heard a complaint, ever, from any one of them. It made my job easy.

Bill grabbed some food from his kit at the truck and opened a can for me. I don't know what it was, but it was so good. I barked for another and got it. He fed me. I deserved it. I was a brave soldier. A soldier.

It wasn't long after that meal that Bill called me to get back in our truck, "Let's go, girl—we're going to work." I liked that because we were always on the go.

We were called the Red Ball Express. As Patton's tanks advanced on the enemy, he needed supplies—fuel, food, water, engine parts, ammo—and we had everything he needed. It was hard to keep up with Patton. The war was moving fast, and we didn't have maps. We followed road markers, red circles the size of a tennis ball painted on walls, trees, rocks to point the way to the stations and the depots for supplies. We didn't have radios. If we didn't see a red ball for a while, we'd have to guess our way there and back.

Going from one place to another was tough, but Corporal Johnson and I were very good traveling without maps. The men would often say, "How did you find this place?"

I was in the lead truck: me, Trixie, and Corporal Johnson. Trixie was a trained soldier. I don't know who trained her, but she was just amazing. She didn't flinch at the sound of guns or explosions. She seemed to know when I needed a lick on the hand to comfort me. I know God sent her to me to keep me safe. I don't know how, but I knew she'd keep me alive, and she proved that a few times.

Bill and Corporal Johnson are talking a little—but we're all pretty tired. I have to close my eyes. I have just seen so much, but all I care about is these men and, especially, SARGE, my Bill. In such a short time, we've become so close. I never think about Mom or the litter now or the other soldiers I've seen or been around. I only think about my Bill. He makes me feel so safe because no matter what happens, he is there to protect me.

We'd go out each day from camp, drive to a depot to get supplies, and we were attacked every time. But we were always lucky. Maybe a few times some gunfire hit one of the trucks—but no one got hurt—never lost a truck. We'd load up—the trucks were loaded and unloaded by German POWs—then we'd drive maybe fifty miles to where Patton's tanks were supposed to be—and they'd be gone. Patton kept moving. We'd get word that Patton was low on supplies, but he just kept rolling. It was very hard to catch up with him.

We'd drop off those supplies at the next depot and then pick up German prisoners to bring back to our camp stockade.

These other soldiers, Germans, they called them, look so sick, so weak. They are very skinny and say nothing. My soldiers are a little nervous around them. I wonder why? The Germans look thirsty and hungry. When they do speak, I don't understand their language. My soldiers keep guns pointed at them. I have to watch everything very carefully. I have to watch my Bill. I have to keep him safe.

To carry the German POW's back to our stockade, they were loaded into the back of our trucks. They were loaded in one at a time, packed very close together—so close they couldn't move their arms or legs. Just when it looked like you couldn't get one more in, more were shoved in.

They had to stand—they had no food or water for the trip. They stood like that for the whole ride back—sometimes fifty, seventy-five, a hundred miles. When we got to our camp stockade, sometimes one or two were dead. They'd died standing up. In the winter, some froze to death.

I felt a little sorry for them sometimes. The treatment was so inhumane, but then I remembered hearing how Americans, our boys, were treated when they were captured (and I heard about the death camps for the Jews). I remember the prayer I said every day and every night.

"Dear God, don't let me get killed over here where no one knows me and don't let me become a prisoner of war with this vicious army. Amen."

I know Trixie heard my silent prayer.

Amen.

A MINE IS DISCOVERED.

There was no mine. Photo of Morris' Unit, The Red Ball Express, during one of their daily runs. Can you find Trixie in the picture sitting on Cpl. Alexander's back?

Chapter Seven
Normandy Camp Headquarters— Memories of Pearl Harbor

This was my life in the Army, or should I say "our" life—Trixie and me. Just about every day, our routine was getting our orders, going to terminals, following the Red Ball, packing up supplies, trying to catch up with Patton's tanks, and taking back prisoners of war.

As I've said, Trixie was quite the little soldier. She went on every detail, knew the routine as well as we did. She had friends all over the camp of every rank and size. Sometimes she'd wander away for a day and I'd think—well, I lost her, but she'd return the next day, happy and looking for her orders.

Camp life is good. We are in our trucks a lot. But sometimes we stay in camp, sleep in our tent, and have the good food our cook makes. He likes me, the cook. I think they call him Mahoffer? He always says to Bill, "Don't forget the dog."

If I hadn't known this was war, I would have felt like it was camping. The guys were relaxed when we were not on the road. Boys away from home, boys—black men—fighting for their country so far away from family and friends and any place they'd known. They did the job without question, without fear. I was so proud to be a part of this group, so proud to be their Sarge.

I like it when they can relax and talk to each other. My Bill talks to them and they listen. But he listens, too. I can tell they like him very much. Sometimes while he's talking, he pats me gently. When I go on one of my adventures during the day, he's so happy to see me when I come back. I love him so much.

It was Hawaii 1941 and we'd all come over together from Camp Steward. One-hundred fifty of us were made sergeants after we did our time at Pearl Harbor.

Pearl Harbor. Seems like a lifetime ago. My God, that was the first time I witnessed the horror of war. The first time war was brought to our shores.

I was on a leave from Camp Edwards, home with my girlfriend, Norcie Allen. It was December 7, 1941. The radio was on; we were having breakfast—enjoying being together, laughing, planning our future—then the music stopped. The announcer sounded scared, frantic, "All military are to report to their units immediately. Pearl Harbor has been bombed. The Japanese have just attacked Pearl Harbor."

Where the hell was Pearl Harbor? Didn't matter, I kissed Norcie, grabbed my coat and rushed out the door.

At the Staten Island ferry, all you could see were soldiers and sailors. All transportation—boats, buses, taxis, trains—were for military only, and they were packed.

They bombed our navy. So many were dead.

When I got back to Camp Edwards, everyone was running around like crazy. We were scared, all of us. There was a bridge called Buzzards Bay in Massachusetts. We set up our big guns on the bridge, aimed them across the water, and waited for enemy planes. Soldiers in trucks patrolled along the bridges and streets. We waited and waited.

I wondered how secure the people of Buzzards Bay felt. They could clearly see the guns and the military all around. What they didn't know was that those big guns trained on the sky to keep them safe *had no ammunition.*

We had no bullets, no cannon balls. All this was for show to comfort the American people.

After a day of that, we went back to our barracks and packed our bags. We were moving out. We marched to a train and were loaded on along with our guns and trucks. We were on the train for a few weeks. It took as long as it wanted to get us to San Francisco. From there we were taken to Lockheed, a factory that made planes. We slept there, in this huge hanger. for two days. Then we shipped out again.

This time we marched about three miles to the waterfront. There was a huge ship loading thousands of soldiers. I was told to wait to hear my name, and shortly I heard, "Morris, William Jr."

I walked up the gangplank, "Morris, William A. Jr. 20266"

It took a few days to load that ship. I was in my room lying in my bunk, moaning with seasickness from all the rocking in the harbor while the boat was loading.

All of a sudden, one of my buddies ran into the room, "Morris, enemy airplanes have been spotted. Everybody has to go on deck."

I grabbed my rifle and helmet and ran up the stairs, two at a time, to the top deck.

When I got out there, all the guys were laughing at me.

"Morris, for a seasick guy you can really move. And how seasick can you be? We haven't left the dock yet."

The ship was still at the dock. I felt like a chump, but I had to laugh at myself. That temporarily cured my seasickness.

We didn't know where we were going. No one had ever heard of Pearl Harbor, at least I never had. But a few weeks later, we got to Pearl.

We sailed into one of the worst sights I have ever seen.

It was two weeks after the bombing; we were the first unit to arrive. Oh my God, I'll never forget the sight. Ships were on their sides in the still smoldering harbor. Buildings destroyed, our planes blown apart. Whole areas were destroyed and some were still on fire.

Our ship was unloaded quickly; guns were set up right away. I was driving a truck, and then a few days later, I was transferred to the motor pool. In only a few hours, I heard guns going off. They were being tested, shooting out over the ocean, securing the area. Once we arrived, it only took a couple of hours before we had 50-caliber guns good for antiaircraft put in place for action. We were just about the only combat regiment there.

My job was with the motor pool. We were in charge of hauling material for the building of a new airfield, Hickam Field. There were two thousand men working on that airfield. I was there for over a year, no leave, no days off. But in spite of that it was great, in many ways, the girls (oh, boy) and the food. They made up for everything else.

I didn't see much of Hawaii—there was too much to do.

We were only allowed to go one mile from the base. Black soldiers did not get visits from the Hollywood stars or the USO shows. All the Hollywood entertainment was for the white soldiers—although we had plenty of entertainment by the Hawaiian people and those beautiful hula girls. But, I can say, the food was good. No K-rations—good food and luaus on the base. I had so much pineapple that I never have to eat one, ever again.

One day, there was a big commotion by the barracks wall. Everyone was saying a list was up and my name was on it: "Morris, William A., Jr., corporal promoted to sergeant in charge of the motor pool."

What? I was now in charge of all the trucks, jeeps and any moving vehicle that they were getting.

There were 150 names on the list. One hundred fifty brand new Black American sergeants. I was so proud of that. All this happened because of my training back home in Morris Moving on those moving trucks.

But there was no pineapple here in France, 1944—no palm trees, hula skirts, or luaus. Here, when we were on the road we were cold, eating rations; only when we got to camp did we have a warm cot. Here every night, as we tossed and turned in our sleep, we relived that horrible day on the beach of death, but we never spoke of it. We didn't have to; it was in our eyes. Each of us would carry that scene to our grave. Carry it in our heads, hearts, and souls until our dying day. Only the exhaustion of our assignments each day kept us from having worse nightmares. Maybe that's why we pushed on. Maybe that's why we never questioned or complained. We'd survive here. We'd seen boys our age dying in foreign water. We'd seen friends blown apart—arms and legs strewn across a golden stretch of sand. We'd heard the screams and pleas for help unanswered. All this we never spoke of, but we would never forget.

I love being around the soldiers. When I wander during the day, I visit other soldiers near us. They are all young. They all pet me. Give me food, water. I play with them. I listen to their stories. Some of them seem very sad, so I give them an extra lick on the hand. It seems to help, but my home is with Bill, so I never stay away too long.

Sometimes during the night, I hear cries. Sometimes Bill will mumble, turn over a lot. I think it's about that day, the day of the big noise and the blood. I sometimes lick his hand to quiet him when this happens. I can feel how that day changed all of them. Dogs know that. We can tell when the hurt is deep. We can sense it. I think I help them forget about it. I think I help them remember not every day was like that one.

*369th Coast Artillery Unit leaving San Francisco for Pearl Harbor.
One of the first units sent to Hawaii after Dec 7, 1941 attack.*

Chapter Eight
Trixie's Hit

I remember it was a particularly beautiful morning, peaceful. The air smelled good. It was one of those days I had time to be thankful I was alive.

We'd just finished breakfast, and I was heading back to the trucks when I heard it. I heard a strange whistling sound, a bomb. What the hell? One of ours? One of theirs? Didn't matter, it was coming fast and coming into camp. "Take cover." Hit the deck.

"BOMB! BOMB!"

We ran for cover, everywhere and anywhere. It hit a few feet away from the main area. Metal, dust everywhere, then that awful silence until someone yelled, "All clear. Is everyone okay?"

I checked myself—I was in one piece. All around me the guys were signaling they were fine, and then I heard it, a sound that hit my heart like a knife. A whimpering came from behind me. I turned to see Trixie lying on her side, covered in blood. She'd been hit.

My leg. My leg. Something in me...it's something burning hot. I can't move. Help me, Bill. Help me.

Trixie's hit. Trixie's been hit. I heard myself screaming—screaming as if it was me or one of my guys—and it was. It was Trixie. The men came running. "Trixie's hit Get the jeep!" I picked her up, and carried her to the jeep, already running with Corporal Johnson at the wheel. Soldiers surrounded us, running alongside as long as they could. Some were crying. I had no idea all these guys knew my dog. It was like they had been saving up these tears since D-Day. That even though they'd seen such horror, this bleeding little dog had given them license to cry. I glanced around and saw men on their knees praying. Others looked up to the heavens, and others were in shock. Our Trixie was hit.

The pain is really, really bad. The jeep is going so fast. Every bump hurts so much. Bill keeps petting me, saying, "It's OK, girl. Hold on, Trixie. Just hold on, girl." I will hold on. I will, for him.

It was only about a quarter mile away to the medics, but it felt like a hundred miles. Trixie's leg was bleeding badly. She was whining but managed to lick my hand. I jumped from the jeep before it stopped and ran into the medic's tent. "Doc. Doc. Trixie's been hit. Her leg is bleeding. Please help her."

The doctor took a look at her and yelled, "She's a dog. I treat soldiers not dogs."

I couldn't believe it. "Trixie is a soldier!" I shouted, but knew there was no use arguing. Jumping back into the jeep, I told Corporal Johnson to take us to headquarters. The corporal gave me a look. I was breaking protocol. Trixie was dying—I didn't care. The chain of command was for me to go to the first sergeant, then the second lieutenant, then the major, then the colonel. I was going straight to the colonel. I had no time for Army protocol.

I didn't care what it meant. Trixie was dying. Leaving Trixie in the jeep with the corporal, I went into headquarters and right up to the colonel. "Sir, I'm sorry, sir, but Trixie's been hit, and the doc refuses to treat her. She got hit in the grenade attack, shrapnel. She's bleeding. She's dying."

His usually calm demeanor changed when he heard about Trixie.

"Sergeant, go straight back to the medic. Trust me, when you get there the doctor will take care of our Trixie."

The jeep ride back seemed to take seconds this time, and when we arrived at the medical tent, the doctor was standing outside waiting. He said nothing to me but gently took Trixie from my arms and ordered his team to get busy and save this dog.

I knew that if anything bad happened to Trixie, the outcome of our time in this war would be changed forever. The heart and spirit of my men and I would be torn from us.

They took me from Bill. So many people running around. Someone is wiping my leg. Oh, it hurts so much. They put something on me to stop the pain. But where is Bill? Where is Corporal Johnson? Where am I?

�֍

It took a while; they wouldn't let me come in. I couldn't see her while they worked on her, but I could tell Trixie was being cared for like a soldier. Finally, the doctor called me in, and a few other guys went in with me. I was so scared I could just barely walk.

She wagged her tail slightly as I got to her. Her leg was bandaged. I could see bloody shrapnel in a bowl next to her.

I wanted to cry with tears of joy. She's going to be all right.

"She's going to be fine," said the doctor. "I'm so sorry what happened before. When you first came in all I saw was a dog. I didn't know...I didn't know how important this dog is. I feel so small and hurt. Again, forgive me."

I nodded. All I cared about was that Trixie was going to live.

"Here are some pills to prevent infection. Change the bandage daily. Try to keep her quiet, and stay in touch with me."

Bill picked me up gently. Whatever they gave me, I was a little tired, but more than anything I felt safe and loved, oh so loved. Bill gently carried me to the jeep. There are other soldiers around us. "How is she? She gonna be all right?" Bill just nods and pats me. "We're going home now, girl. You're gonna be okay."

They drove back so slowly. I could tell they were being very careful, avoiding holes and bumps.

Well, I didn't get court marshaled for breaking the chain of command. That's the second time I got away with that while in the army.

As I put Trixie to bed in my tent, I remembered that other time. Boy, God sure looks out for me. I feel like one of His people.

In 1940, I was stationed at Camp Edwards in Massachusetts. We were getting ready to go out on maneuvers. We'd be gone from base a few days. Suddenly I got this toothache, and it just got worse and worse. I went to sick call, and the dentist said he really couldn't do anything. All his equipment was packed up for the maneuvers. He said I'd have to wait until Tuesday, and this was Saturday.

My whole head was pounding; I went to the first sergeant. He told me to just stay in the barracks all weekend, don't go on maneuvers.

The pain was too much. Around 4 p.m., everyone had left camp except the guards. I got dressed and climbed through a hole in the fence. I went AWOL. Absent Without Leave.

I left camp and ran to the train station, got to New York, took the ferry, and got to my home town, Staten Island. I took a bus to my dentist, Dr. Marrow. When I got there, it was about 8:30 p.m. He was known to stay late sometimes, and luckily this was one of those nights. He was just leaving his office.

He was shocked to see me.

"What's wrong?"

I explained my dilemma. He didn't hesitate, unlocked his door, and went back into the office.

"Wow, this is a wisdom tooth. With swelling like this, I shouldn't pull it but you need to get back, so I'll pull it and give you some meds for infection and send you on your way".

Ah, the relief was immediate. I never felt so happy to have a dentist—especially one who worked late.

I took out my wallet to pay him, and he shoved my hand away.

"There's no way I can take money from you. You came all the way here, and you are fighting for us. Now get out of here, get back safely, and don't get caught by the MPs."

I made the trek back to the train station, taking a bus and ferry to get there. Just as I was about to board the train, I spotted them, MPs.

They saw me and started walking my way. I couldn't run; that would have been a sure give away I was doing something wrong. But someone stopped them to ask a question. I ducked onto the train and walked to a seat way in the back. The train left two minutes later...whew.

I got back to the base and climbed through the same hole in the fence, undetected. On Monday the regiment came back. If I had gotten caught, in time of war AWOL would mean jail time, no excuses, hard labor, and a dishonorable discharge. No one ever knew.

✻

After Trixie's first night, I left her in my tent sleeping and reported to the first sergeant, Joe Morton. He put us both on light duty until Trixie was healed. "You're now the POW Sergeant." Joe was one of the best men and sergeants I ever met. He was just tops.

Our German POWs were kept in our stockade. There were only about eight POWs now. They had been captured during our daily rounds and somehow there was never any way or time to get them to the general stockade. We weren't even sure where that was, so they stayed.

Our stockade was about fifty or sixty feet long and twenty feet wide. It was enclosed by a high fence that was topped with barbed wire. The back part of the enclosure was a long wooden shed where the prisoners lived. Food was brought to them. My new assignment was sergeant in charge of prisoners, so I had to check the guards every four to five hours. The guards were on rotating shifts, looking over the stockade from the guard tower, which was a shed atop the platform encased in glass that overlooked the entire area. The prisoners were taken out every day to do work.

I was feeling much better, only a little pain if I tried to run. The cook gave me extra meat. "Have to get you well, girl," he said and always gave me an extra pat. Bill tried to keep me quiet, but I wanted to get to see my guys. Finally, he took me to our new assignment.

❋

You needed to climb a ladder to get to the guard tower. Our first day "at work" I looked up at the fifteen-step wooden ladder and looked down at Trixie. I knew she was anxious to get to work, but I also knew she was still healing.

So I picked her up and carried her up to the guard tower. That was a struggle. Trixie wasn't a big dog, but she was no toy poodle. Trixie endured the humiliation of being treated like a baby, but she didn't like it. She really saw herself as a soldier, and she wanted to do her part. Once we got to the tower, she did her job keeping watch over everything. She loved it up there because she could see over the whole camp.

I didn't like being carried. I felt like a pup. I could see my Bill didn't like it either—cook had been feeding me too well. But once we got to the top, it was worth it. The view. I could see everything.

It wasn't a bad assignment, but I knew I couldn't carry Trixie up and down the ladder every day. So I decided she needed to learn how to climb a ladder. We worked slowly over two weeks and every day she got better at it. In two days, she was able to slowly, very slowly climb to the top. After two weeks, Trixie ran up the ladder and took her place in the guard shack. I could see that her leg still hurt and the climb was painful, but she was a trooper. She never quit.

My leg was stiff at first. It was hard for me to step on it and try to climb, but I got stronger. Bill cleaned my wound every day and gave me my pills. I got stronger and walked around the camp more, saying hello to my soldier boys. Everyone was glad to see me—everyone had been praying for me. I felt that I knew how much I meant to them. I hope they know how much they mean to me.

William A. Morris Jr, Pvt, Camp Edwards, Mass.

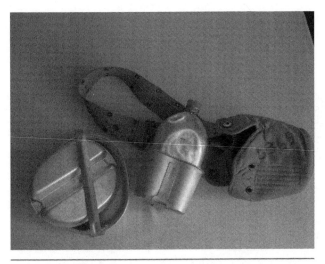

William Morris mess kit issued when he enlisted in the 369ᵗʰ in Harlem and carried throughout the war.

Pvt William A. Morris Jr. on office duty with Pvt Singleton, Camp Edwards, Mass.

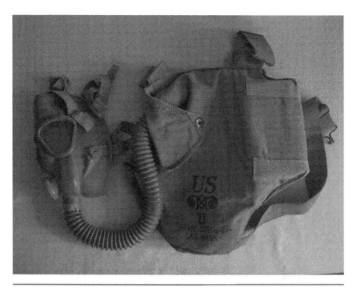

Gas Mask issued to Morris when he enlisted.
It was never used in battle.

Chapter Nine
They Try To Kill My Bill

It's funny, I never really thought about dying, not even on that beach on D-Day. Maybe I always felt God was looking out for me.

I remember at Camp Stewart in 1941 when I was a sergeant and had all these young men looking up to me, trusting me, and I was not much older than most of them. Me? The baby of the family? Junior, as some called me.

I never saw any white officers. I guess they thought we weren't good enough, but we knew better.

Usually when a group of soldiers arrives at camp, there's a parade, a military greeting. Here we were 150 sergeants—officers—all being sent from Pearl, sent to this camp to train soldiers, sent to this camp to prepare young men for battle—and we got no greeting at all. No parade, no band, no welcome. We found our way to our barracks; the barracks had two floors, twenty-nine privates, four or five months broken in, on each side of the room. As you entered, there was a separate room for the sergeant. Reveille was 6 a.m., and when the bugle sounded the first call, the sergeant, me, would open his door and look down both sides to make sure everyone was up.

This one morning, I could see that a soldier in the last bunk was still asleep. I walked up to him and said, "Soldier, reveille. Hit the floor. Let's go."

The soldier didn't move. What the heck? I pulled back his covers and a hand came up from under the sheets and he put a gun to my jaw.

He said, "If you ever wake me up again, I'll blow your head off." And he went back under the covers. I walked past the other men to my room and shut the door. I sat down on the bed, shaking like a leaf, sweat pouring through my clothes. I knew the bugle would blow soon and we would have to go out for inspection.

All of us assembled and the first sergeant called out, "First platoon."

Their sergeant called back, "All present and accounted for."

"Second platoon." I answered, "All present *or* accounted for."

"All present *or* accounted for," I said this for two days. For two days I left that soldier in his bed and did not go near him.

On the third day, a runner came to me and said, "Report to the first sergeant."

I knew why he wanted to see me.

The sergeant got right to the point.

"Why did you say, 'All present *or* accounted for?' Why have you been saying that for the last two days?"

I told him about the soldier, the gun, everything. I said I didn't tell him because I didn't want the soldier locked up. He'd be tried, convicted, put in jail (the brig) and given a dishonorable discharge. He'd never be able to get a job. His life would be ruined.

The first sergeant was very calm.

"Sergeant Morris, tomorrow if you say, 'All present or accounted for,' I will call you out and take your stripes in front of everyone. I will bust you down to private."

I was not going to lose my stripes for anyone. I had earned them with long, hard work. I decided I would take those covers off that soldier tomorrow. I sent for the soldier and told him what the top kick (first sergeant) said. "So, tomorrow I'll be down to your bunk and your covers come off. I'll do my job; you do what you have to do."

The next morning I was ready. At 6 a.m., I opened my door and looked down the line. The soldier was under the covers. I said a silent prayer, "Dear God, walk with me on this, please. I got a problem." I walked down the row, soldier by soldier. I felt their eyes on me, maybe praying for me. I got to the soldier's cot, and I took a deep breath.

"Soldier, reveille, get out from under those covers now. That's an order."

I said this three times.

Then with my heart in my throat, a special prayer on my lips, "Please God, be with me," I reached down and pulled the covers off.

That soldier had the biggest grin on his face I'd ever seen—and he was dressed in his uniform. He said, "See, Sarge. I fooled you."

I said nothing to him, just turned around and walked back to my room. I closed the door. I was shaking and sweating like a pig.

Out on the field, first sergeant called out, "Second platoon."

I said, loud and clear, "All present *and* accounted for, sir."

The first sergeant smiled very slightly, no one else noticed the wink he gave me.

Later, that soldier, I think his name was Harris, came to me.

"Sarge, you know the men have so much respect for you. And I do, too. You will never have any trouble out of me or any of your men. What you did took a lot of guts, I tell everyone, "That's *my* Sarge."

I smiled to myself. I knew God was watching over me. I knew I had done the right thing, and I always believed God does right by those that do right.

Bill's humming, seems happy today. He must be remembering stuff, maybe about his family. Sometimes I think about my family. I wonder where they are. I wonder if they are safe. I wonder if they found their soldier, their Bill.

Like I said, I never saw a white officer. Most of them had not been military trained. They were businessmen, professionals in private life, so when they joined up or got drafted they were made officers. They hadn't had our intense specialized training. They hadn't had our experience. They were intimidated by us, black men and knowing more than they did. They just couldn't stomach it.

It was a lovely morning; at least it started out that way.

We were getting the trucks ready for our daily runs; the trucks were loaded. A jeep pulled up with white officers. This couldn't be good. One of the officers spoke to me.

"Sergeant, drive your truck to the rear of the convoy. I'll lead the trucks."

I was in shock. "Who are you? You're not taking my convoy."

"I'm your commanding officer."

"Sorry, Sir, do you know where to go?"

"Don't question me, soldier."

It was the army; you do what you're told. The corporal looked at me, and so did Trixie. Corporal whispered, "He'll be lost in fifteen minutes."

We drove our truck to the end of the line. Sure enough, in less than fifteen minutes, we were driving around in circles. We'd passed the same tree four times.

I did not like that soldier, that pale one. He did not like my Bill; I could sense the hate on him. Why are we going to the back away from the other trucks? We're first truck, always first truck. Why are we going to the back?

Then a few miles down the road, we came under fire. This was nothing to us—it happened on every run. We thought nothing of this—we never fired back—just kept on driving. But suddenly the convoy stopped. A driver from the front of the convoy came to our truck.

"Captain wants you to come back to the front of the convoy. He said you can take over now."

Corporal Johnson and I swallowed our laughter. Even Trixie seemed to be laughing. We went to our place in the front of our convoy of sixteen trucks.

We arrived at the depot and unloaded our supplies. Because the captain had no idea what to do or what our job was, he told us to head back without picking up any German prisoners. We said nothing to him.

On our way back, the captain must have realized he not only had gotten lost on the way, but he was coming back empty, something we never did.

About halfway back to camp, the captain's jeep came up alongside my truck. What does he want this time, I wondered.

"Sergeant, I have a mission for you and the corporal. The mission is only for you guys. Don't take any other trucks with you; you guys run solo."

I knew immediately what this was. This was a setup, a suicide mission.

I pulled my truck over to the side and drove past the convoy. My men saluted me and the corporal as I passed. They knew exactly what this was. We were being sent out to die.

Something is wrong. I can tell. I can smell the fear. My Bill and Corporal Johnson are not happy. They are strangely silent. Why are we driving away from the others? Where are we going?

We drove to this terminal as the captain had instructed. The soldiers there had no idea what we were talking about. There was no package to pick up, and they'd never heard of this captain.

It didn't surprise us. We headed back to camp, watching for the red ball to help us find our way. We weren't sure where we were, and it was getting late. We were getting tired, so we decided pull over into this field about the size of a football field surrounded by trees. We took our guns, gas masks, helmets, and went under our truck to sleep. It was a nice summer evening.

I'm so glad we stopped. I needed a nap. My Bill always knows when it is time. He gave me some water, a little food, and we went under the truck. I didn't mind sleeping under the truck. It was warm and safe. I went to sleep right away. It had been a long day. It felt so good to rest. I wasn't asleep very long, I don't think, but it had to be dawn by now. I smell something. I see something coming out of the woods.

Trixie never barked; so when I heard her soft growl, I knew something was very wrong. I sat up and patted her to quiet her, but she continued her soft growl. I looked out to where she was looking and then I saw them, three pairs of German boots coming towards us. I signaled the corporal to grab our guns. We couldn't go to the front of the truck. We needed to crawl to the back, to the side next to the woods so they would not see us as they came up. We started crawling on our bellies. I looked back and almost laughed out loud. Trixie was crawling on her belly, too. Where did she learn this?

We could hear the Germans tearing the truck apart, looking for supplies, food, guns, anything—above all sweets and chocolates.

My heart is pounding. Those other soldiers are the bad ones. I know this. I've seen them before. My Bill and Corporal Johnson are very quiet. I am, too. They are ready. I am, too.

Now we crawled to the side of the truck closer to the front. Then we got in position, ready to fire. I tapped Corporal Johnson and said, "You take him. I'll take the other, and maybe the two of us can get the one in the middle." Corporal Johnson and I shot at almost the same time, and both German soldiers went down. But the one in the middle had his gun on Johnson and me, and that's when Trixie took over.

Trixie jumped in the air and bit the German's arm. His gun went flying, and we shot him down. Trixie saved us.

We were taught in training that when you come in contact with any enemy, you don't stop and ask yourself, "Is he going to shoot?" or any other questions. We were taught to kill or be killed. We carried out our duty.

We made sure they were dead. I took the belt with the German insignia on it from the third soldier and one of their flags that was just lying there. We ran back to the truck and drove out of there fast. We were not sure if we had crossed enemy lines; we were not sure where the hell we were.

The problem was we couldn't fine the red ball. We drove around for miles. Finally, Corporal Johnson spotted it—a red ball painted on a tree.

"There it is. We can breathe easier now, Sarge. Home can't be far away now."

I've done a good thing. My Bill and Corporal Johnson were safe. They patted me all the way back. "Good girl... good girl." I feel like a real soldier—because I am.

When we finally got back to camp, the men surrounded our truck, pats on the back, smiles, laughter, they were so glad to see us, and we'd never been happier to see them. My blood slowly started to boil now that I had time to realize what this jerk of a captain had done. I couldn't believe it.

I reported to the first sergeant, who said, "The captain won't be happy to see you."

I asked permission to report my return to the captain myself and got it.

I walked into the headquarters tent and approached him.

"We're back, Sir, mission accomplished."

He stared at me, shocked, sweat started to pour from his head. He was speechless. I turned and left, smiling to myself. I never told him what happened in the woods.

I thought no more about it until I was alone and it was relatively quiet. It came to me that I had taken a life. I could picture the face of the soldier I had killed. He was a kid like me, about the same age. He had blonde hair; his face was very smooth with a few blonde hairs on his face above his lip. He must have been trying to grow a mustache. I remember his blue eyes before he fell.

You wonder how I saw all of this in that split second before I killed him. It became etched in my brain and became clear later.

Killing someone is not fun. I always heard tough guys and guys in the movies say, "I'm gonna kill him or shoot him." Then after they do it, they think it's over. But when it's quiet and they are alone and can think, it won't leave them.

That scene, that soldier will stay with me the rest of my life. I didn't feel like a hero. I was glad to be alive, but I will never forget that face.

Captured Nazi Flag.

Chapter Ten
Days Off

I wouldn't say the Army was fun, but there were times when we could forget for a little while that we were at war.

I recall Camp Stewart again in 1941, Georgia.

Camp Stewart was one of the most racist Army camps in existence.

We arrived fresh from defending our country at Pearl Harbor, fresh from rebuilding the airfield to being treated like dogs, not like heroes.

All the officers were white, young, and inexperienced.

I paid no attention to their rudeness, prejudice, and insults. I had a job to do.

My job was to train soldiers to drive trucks, and not just to drive, but to drive in unbelievable conditions.

First, my soldiers were taught to grease their truck engines with very specific grease. Every part of the engine had to be covered. Then the trucks were tested in the water.

The training was very specific and strenuous. Each group was taught to drive trucks into a river. They had to keep driving to a flag out in the middle of the river. The water would be up to their necks. Then they had to turn around and drive back. They had to drive in mud, sand, up hills, dodging boulders, dodging explosions. They never asked why.

Of course, on D- Day we found out why.

This one day I had gone to see the first sergeant. I had left the men busy greasing their engines in the motor pool garage.

When I returned, I opened the door to the garage and what I saw made me fall down laughing.

The men were having a grease fight.

Grease was everywhere. I tried to stop it and turned to get a face full of grease. Okay, that did it. I joined in. Grown men enjoying themselves like kids—giving themselves time to forget for just a little while.

After thirty or forty minutes, I had to get serious. "OK, that's enough guys. No one will ever know about this, trust me. But we've got to get cleaned up for evening parade."

The grease was put away; everyone was still smiling as they piled out of the garage.

About two hours later, the platoon assembled for inspection before the evening parade. They all looked perfect. No one could suspect what they'd all looked like only an hour before.

It was moments like these I could forget why we were here—away from our families and stationed in Georgia. Luckily, we didn't have to stay in Camp Stewart much longer.

Some days when my Bill was busy or he was playing cards with the guys, I'd go off on what I called my visit runs. I'd walk all over our camp and to other nearby camps visiting other soldiers. I'd play with them for a while, get some treats, rest in their tents, and then, before lunch time, I'd head back to our camp and to my Bill.

He didn't seem worried that I'd gone for the day—after the first time I did it. He knew I'd come back.

He'd say, "Girl—where ya been? Where'd ya go today?" And then he'd just hug and pat me. I wish I could talk to him. I wish I could tell about the other soldiers, how they missed home, worried about getting hurt or dying, just like my guys, but all I could do was lick him and let him feel the love.

✄

Trixie was with me ninety percent of the time; she went on all our truck runs, slept with me, went to church with me, ate with me, and hung out with the guys. But some days she'd kind of give me a lick goodbye and take off. The first time I kind of panicked. Did she run away? Was she hurt? Did the enemy get her? But then she'd come back a few days later, happy and acting like nothing happened. I didn't have time to follow her and no one seemed to know where she went on these mysterious trips.

One day, we were at one of the depots picking up supplies. Another platoon drove up—and all the soldiers knew Trixie.

She ran to them, licking hands, jumping on them, and giving them a big greeting.

I was shocked. "You guys know my dog?"

Each of the soldiers knew her. She visited them and apparently visited a lot of other camps. She brought a piece of home to these guys, just like she'd done for us.

Each group of soldiers had a different name for Trixie, and she ran to them when she was called Shep or Maxie, but she always came back to me.

When I think about it, Trixie was like our own USO. Since the USO never visited the black troops, I think most of us preferred our little furry soldier. No one can know the comfort of that wet nose next to your face at night as you faced war and possible death every day.

I love running to my other soldier friends. I didn't care what name they gave me; they were young soldiers like my Bill. Sometimes I stayed with them for a day or two. I wander through their camp, but I always come home to my Bill.

Trixie wandered maybe eight or ten miles from our camp to visit these guys. I don't know how she found them, and I don't know how she found her way back. But she did every time. She was always back by Sunday, for church. Don't ask me how she knew it was Sunday—she just did.

Sunday was usually a quiet day. Because I was raised going to church on Sunday, even though I was at war, I went to church. It would catch me off guard sometimes to remember the last time I was in a church at home, my wedding day.

I had known my wife since we were teenagers. Although she was a country girl from Stafford, Virginia, she had spent her summers with her older sisters on Staten Island. That's when I first spotted her; I think I was selling ice cream for a church fundraiser or something. I was about fifteen, and she was the most beautiful girl I had ever seen.

We dated on and off, always well chaperoned. Well, we both had large families to look out for us, but we were pretty certain about getting married. So by the time I had enlisted, we were sort of engaged. Norcie was now living in Staten Island. Once she graduated from high school in Virginia, she was able to get a job as a nanny, along with two of her sisters, taking care of the children of a doctor based at the Quarantine Station in Staten Island. Norcie went to school at night for her nursing degree, and soon she got a job as a nurse for a chiropodist.

I was home after Pearl Harbor on a leave from Camp Stewart. It was clear I'd be shipped out overseas in the next few days. So one day I just said, "Want to get married?'

It was a Saturday, November 20, 1944.

We went to Borough Hall to get a license, but of course, it was closed.

A clerk, just leaving the building, told us where we could find the man that did the licenses. God was looking out for us. Stuff like this would never happen now, but back then, in a small town, a soldier got favors.

We drove to Tottenville, Staten Island, where this man lived, and I told him I was about to be shipped overseas and that we wanted to get married.

Well, believe it or not, he drove back with us to Borough Hall, opened up his office and gave us a license.

By now it was about 8 p.m. We went to our church, Bethel AME Zion, to see our pastor, Rev. Anzapanza Johnson. We told him we wanted to get married. Thinking we were there for couples counseling, he started to usher us into his office so we could talk about setting a date, etc., when I had to stop him.

"No, Reverend, I'm shipping out tomorrow. We have to get married NOW."

Startled, he agreed, but said we needed witnesses. I noted that the choir was practicing in the sanctuary.

"Can we use the choir?"

Sure enough, we had our witnesses.

Now my baby sister, Evelyn, was in the choir. As everyone was rushing around getting the church set up for our little wedding she seemed to disappear. Then, just as suddenly, she reappeared with a secret smile on her face.

Just about a half hour into the ceremony, the doors to the church swung open and my parents marched down the aisle.

My sister must have called them. It was so wonderful to have them be a part of our wedding.

We had an impromptu reception of sorts and a five-hour honeymoon. I shipped out for Europe the next day.

⁂

So yes, it had been awhile since I'd been to regular church. But here in this place, I had to go every Sunday. Part of it stemmed from my childhood ritual where we went to church every Sunday. Being at war, I felt I had to go pray for protection.

In a clearing a little way from our camp, there was a tent. That's where the chaplain was; that was church. We drove off the road into the clearing and walked to the tent. Rows of chairs were set up; a simple altar was in the front. The service wasn't long, maybe fifteen or twenty minutes. Trixie sat by my side, as always. No one cared that a dog had come to church. We'd sing maybe two or three hymns, say prayers, and the chaplain would ask for any special requests. Usually the prayers were for fallen buddies, for folks back home, or for keeping safe. I always prayed silently for my loved ones, my wife, my family, and always I prayed to get home in one piece. I also thanked God for my guardian angel, Trixie.

I like this place. I come here with my Bill and the guys. It's quiet; it's peaceful. I can feel their hearts are lighter here. Bill has a good singing voice. I'd love to have sung too, but my voice isn't good. I just sit quietly by my Bill. I pray like everyone else. I pray that everyone stays alive, especially my Bill. Amen.

Norcie Allen Morris in a glamour pose.

Private Morris, a photo sent to his bride.

Chapter Eleven
Snow and Blood: The Battle of the Bulge

It was December 1944. We were enduring bitter cold in Northwestern Europe and the war was intense.

Our trucks had no heat, no windows, and no seat belts, but we kept doing our runs. We kept going to depots for supplies and prisoners, kept trying to catch up with General Patton's tanks. Sometimes the snow was so deep we had to dig out our trucks with our helmets.

We drove all day, sometimes getting out to dig out our tires or just to walk around to warm up. We wore every piece of clothing we had. Man, it was cold.

My guys didn't like this stuff called snow, but I loved it. I loved helping them dig. Sometimes, my Bill would throw a ball of it at me, but when I grabbed the ball in my mouth, it would fall apart.

Patton's tanks had to keep rolling. The Germans were advancing on the port of Antwerp in a surprise move that left Patton scrambling to the defense. We knew they had to be running out of supplies—food, clothing, and fuel. That's why we kept going to catch up with them.

But the weather was brutal. Continuous snow, temps below zero. And fog, so heavy at times that we couldn't see where we were going.

We drove until we were exhausted. Somewhere near the Ardennes Forest, I think, we just had to stop. All of us were just too tired to go on.

I told the men to find a place, any place, and get some sleep. Some just dropped where they stood, dropped down and immediately fell into a deep sleep. I saw a tree trunk with out-stretched branches not too far away that looked good to me and I lay down. Trixie kept pulling at my leg and backing away. I thought she wanted to play, but that was a bad time, and I was exhausted. I'm surprised we all didn't freeze to death.

No Bill, no, not there. Something is wrong, no Bill. No.

Trixie never acted like that before. This was no time for play. "Not now, girl." I was so tired. I had just lain down against the tree. For the first time, Trixie lay down away from me.

I was not sure how long I slept, but it was light when I woke up. I called out to my men to wake up. "Let's roll." Trixie was sitting up, staring at me. It was then I saw why.

I hadn't been sleeping on a branch or a tree trunk; I had slept on a dead American soldier.

He'd been shot. His frozen arms stuck out like branches. The snow had covered most of him.

Oh my God. The prayers I had been saying this entire war had not graced this soul. Here was an American boy, a son of America like me, dead and frozen, alone on foreign soil.

I gently brushed the snow from his face. He was white and he was young. His color didn't matter. I found his tags and made sure he could be identified and brought back to the burial unit. I bowed my head and so did Trixie. We prayed together for this boy and then moved on.

We continued on in the snow and hard weather. It was clear we were getting close to the front lines. We heard gun fire. A battle was going on up ahead.

Should we go on? The Quartermaster units weren't officially expected to see action.

I signaled to the convoy to pull over and gathered the men around me.

"We're at the front lines. The tanks are up ahead. You know they need the supplies, but we will have to fight. It's up to you. We can go back. I'll walk away, and you guys make a decision. I won't force you to go onwards. We could unload and go back to the depot." I reminded them that we did not get any combat training and this would not be an easy assignment. "This was a matter of life and death. If we go, some of you may die."

I walked away with Trixie, maybe ten steps, when I heard,

"Sarge, let's roll."

I was so proud of these men. They were willing to die. They were willing to give the ultimate sacrifice.

So we dug out the trucks, and I bundled Trixie up in whatever I could find. What a trooper she was; she never complained. She just wanted to be with us. She just wanted to be with me.

My Bill keeps wrapping me up in blankets and some of his clothes, but I'm okay. I feel excited. Something is about to happen. I hear that sound, almost like that day on the beach. I see smoke. Why are we going there? I smell danger.

We were at the front. I could barely see the outline of the tanks. They're covered with snow.

Patton's tank Army had been in this harsh weather, this snow and cold, for forty-one days fighting the German Army. The Germans wanted Antwerp, a very important port. The Americans had held eighty-five miles along this defensive front, but the Germans had made a push, bending the front line like a bulge; that's where this battle got its name.

Our convoy pulled up and we were surrounded by our army. We were welcomed by the troops. They did not care that we were black soldiers.

They were hungry, cold, and without ammunition. We begin unloading supplies immediately, taking turns warming up by the mess tent fires. Some of the POWs from the tank corps helped unload as well. We stayed in the mess area most of the day to get some rest. It felt so good.

The cooks went to work and cooked a hot meal for all the troops. As we sat around resting up, orders came over the loud speaker, "Man your guns."

I finally get a chance to rest with my Bill. We eat together and play a little. I don't miss my family anymore because my Bill is my family. He pets me all the time, tells me I'm good, and thanks me for taking care of him.

I ran outside to my men. We all grabbed our guns. We were told to get to a certain area and just fire our guns. Just fire them anywhere. We started firing at nothing.

The tanks were firing; the noise was unbelievable.

Later, I was told that the Germans had made a push. Our aircrafts were grounded because of bad weather. Our army was in big trouble.

Firing all day, as we were doing, made the Germans think reinforcements had arrived.

We kept firing our rifles; sometimes we fired them lying on our backs or over our shoulders. No one cared; we just had to keep firing.

That noise went on all day and all night. It didn't bother me. I didn't even care about the big noise that came from those steel

things they called tanks. I just stood by my Bill. When he ate, I ate. When he moved, I moved.

After two days, we took back over 200 prisoners. We drove fifty miles or more before we stopped. Those POWs were out in the open in the back of our trucks. Many of them froze to death.

We were exhausted when we finally made our way back to our camp, but we held our heads high.

We had survived another battle. The Germans thought they had us. The front lines had been weakened by that German push, but our boys held strong. We held Antwerp.

I found out later that the Germans had gone into hospitals in other towns and killed soldiers and patients there. This cruelty was in retaliation for the battle we had won, the horror of war. I will never understand how men can act this way toward one another.

But, we'd done our part and again the good Lord had seen fit to get us home safe.

Chapter Twelve
They Try To Kill Him... Again

About a month after the Battle of the Bulge, that white captain who had remained strangely out of sight from us made another appearance.

Just like before, he announced he was taking my convoy out again.

I shook my head. Didn't he learn his lesson? What was the reason for this? He still had no idea what he was doing.

I started up my truck just as the captain approached.

"Corporal, go to one of the trucks in the back of the convoy and ride shotgun."

"Sergeant, you're going to take your truck out alone, solo. You don't need any of your trucks. This is a special mission to retrieve a package."

Oh my God. This was murder. He was sending me out alone.

For the first time, I was scared to death.

Just as I drove past the convoy, the men saluted me. Corporal Johnson nodded as if to say, "We're with you, Sarge. God speed."

I patted Trixie. Thank God she was with me.

"Here we go, girl."

My Bill is scared. I am too. Where is Corporal Johnson? Why are we going out without the others again? I lick Bill's hand, so glad we were together.

Of course when I reached the depot, there was no package to pick up. No one knew what I was talking about. So I headed back, looking for the red ball, but after driving awhile I wasn't sure where we were. My eyes were getting heavy, but I didn't dare pull over to sleep.

"We'll just stretch our legs, girl."

Trixie and I got out of the truck and walked a little way into the clearing. It was a beautiful day. We walked a bit further then Trixie suddenly stopped short.

Something, someone is in the woods. Someone is coming.

A German soldier stepped out of the woods. He just stood there.

Trixie didn't growl or move.

We just stood there, staring at each other.

Slowly the German took the rifle he had at his side and pushed it a little away from his body.

I did the same.

He moved his rifle a little further away from his side.

So did I.

Finally, he took one step back.

So did I.

Trixie mirrored my movements and stepped back a little just as I did.

The soldier stepped back again and again until he disappeared into the woods.

Trixie and I jumped into the truck and took off.

We drove and drove, still searching for the red ball. Were we behind enemy lines? Would we run into more Germans? I drove and prayed, and out of nowhere, there it was, a red ball. What a blessed night. It was a little faded, but that was definitely a red ball. Thank you, Lord.

About an hour later, we arrived at camp. The men dropped everything and ran to our truck. They patted me on the back. "Good to see you, Sarge. We knew you'd make it."

Corporal Johnson shook my hand, fighting back tears. He knelt to pat Trixie and looked up at me, "Welcome home, Sarge. Welcome home."

We're back. We're back. So many hugs, so many pats. I think some are crying. There's Corporal Johnson—my wonderful Corporal Johnson.

I didn't stop to sleep or eat but marched straight to the captain's tent.

"I'm back, sir. I have nothing for you."

The man was white, but turned pale. He never spoke, just nodded. I'm sure he was thinking, "I can't kill this guy."

I saluted and left him.

I never reported the incident to anyone.

Chapter Thirteen
Going Home—Summer 1945

A year. I couldn't believe we'd been here a year. We'd been too busy to count days. I don't think I looked at a watch or a calendar since I got here.

It was summer at last. The winter seemed to go on forever, but thank God it ended, and the warmth of the sun felt so good. I was just getting ready to go to the trucks when I saw our first sergeant approaching.

First Sgt. Joseph Morton, I'll never forget him. He had been our leader this whole time. We'd only seen white officers twice (when they attempted to get me killed). First Sergeant Morton was our connection to command.

"Morris, get your guys together. I've got news."

I couldn't imagine what news; the army was full of surprises.

I got the men together; we made a circle around the sergeant.

"I have good news. You're going home, all of you, the whole unit. Start getting ready. Good job."

Going home.

I'm not sure what's happening. Everyone seems very excited, very happy. My Bill keeps saying, "We're going home, girl." I'm not sure what that means. This has been my home.

The Army figured out who went home using a point system. The points were decided by length of time served overseas, number of battles, and type of battle. Our group had enough points to be one of the first to be sent home. All those supply runs we did every day under fire counted for something.

Trixie was a little confused by all this. I could see it in her eyes when I told her we're going home. This camp had been our home. These guys had been our family. I can't remember what life was like before the army, before driving in mud and snow, dodging bullets, and seeing death.

The fighting had stopped here, so we were able to do a little relaxing before going home. A few of us, four to be exact, went into town, or what we called a town, to a little store that sold sodas. We were there awhile, just hanging out, talking about what we'd do when we got home, stuff like that, when about six white army soldiers came in. They gave us dirty looks and called us a few things that we ignored.

But they kept on, until one of the white soldiers got up in the face of one of our guys and shoved him. The fight started. Fists flew, and it went on for a while.

Trixie stayed out of the way. I didn't want her hurt. She must have been confused to see our soldiers fighting each other.

What is going on? My Bill and his friends are fighting. Should I help them? Should I bite one of these other soldiers? I don't know what to do. I just have to keep watching Bill.

✂

Then someone said the MPs were on their way. I yelled to my men, "Let's go," and we left and made our way down the road to a bombed out building and hid. We peeked out. There were the white MPs. If they'd seen us, we wouldn't have stood a chance. No matter what story we told them, we would be the ones arrested. After all we'd been through, it was clear—nothing had changed.

We waited until we saw the white soldiers being led away by the MPs, and then we made our way back to camp.

It took about two days for us to be called together again. This time there were trucks waiting for us. We boarded the trucks for the trip from Normandy to England, South Hampton, where we first landed so long ago.

Trixie and I got in the first truck with our gear. Everyone had a huge grin on his face. We could hardly believe it. The talk was about home, seeing family again, eating good old soul food, wearing civilian clothes. After we landed, they drove us to a dock about an hour away where a kind of camp had been set up. More and more soldiers were arriving.

My unit found a place to wait. We stood around together; we were so excited, talking about home.

Trixie was visiting with all her soldiers. I couldn't wait to have her meet my wife, my family, and my friends.

One of the guys was scratching Trixie behind her ears, one of her favorite things, when he looked up at me and said, "This is going to be hard, Sarge. How are you going to leave her?"

Leave her. It never occurred to me to leave Trixie here.

Then other guys in the unit started saying the same thing.

"You can't take her with you."

"How could you ever get her home?"

"They're not going to let her get on the boat."

I panicked. My body went numb. Leave her? That will never happen. I'd have to stay here, in England and become an English citizen. I was not going to abandon my best friend.

Suddenly, I got an idea.

I love these guys. They are so happy right now, but Bill seems worried. All of a sudden, he leans down to me and points to his bag.

"Get in, girl, and keep very quiet. Don't make a sound. Please don't make a sound."

I emptied my duffel bag. Everyone got the idea immediately; I didn't have to say anything. The guys picked up my stuff and put it in their bags. I put Trixie in the duffel. She looked confused, but then I told her she'd have to be quiet. I could see she understood. I zipped my bag shut just as I heard my name called, and I ran up the gangplank.

"Morris, William A. Jr. 20266"

I was given a room assignment on the ship—we had four soldiers to a room. We were all sergeants, all from my same camp.

I let out a huge sigh of relief and opened the duffel. Trixie popped up and looked around.

Where am I now? Well, it doesn't matter, there's my Bill, smiling and patting me. He said I still have to be quiet and stay out of sight. I don't care. As long as I'm with him, I know I'll be fine.

I kept Trixie in the room until the ship sailed. My roommates had no problem with their room "guest." We went to sea about two days later. All the guys that knew I'd brought her on board kept our secret.

Once we left the dock and we were on the ocean, I gave her the okay. "Okay, girl, this ship is yours," and boy, did she make it her ship.

Bill told me it was okay to go and so I did.

I ran from our room. It seemed like I'd been cooped up in there forever. This place was huge. We were on water like that day on the beach, but it was different. I love it.

There are men of different colors on this thing my Bill called "a ship." Everyone is so good to me. I made new friends every day. I am never hungry or thirsty. Everyone makes sure I have food. This "ship" was a new adventure, but not like the other time we were on the water. This time I never feel danger. I don't hear those big "gun" noises.

※

Trixie went everywhere, except the galley where we ate. I figured I'd be pushing my luck if I allowed her in there. I never heard any complaint about "the dog on the ship."

In fact, I'd see white sailors, officers, everyone smiling when they saw her. No one questioned her presence.

And as always, Trixie found her way back to our room every night and slept by my side.

I'm not sure how long we were at sea. I know it was a shorter trip than the one when I came over a year ago.

During one of our daily card games, we started talking about where we would soon land. Some guys said Fort Dix, New Jersey. My mouth dropped open. FORT DIX? Next to Camp Stewart, that was one of the most racist bases in the army. They'd kill Trixie there—just because she belonged to me. My head was spinning. I wondered, "What do I do now?"

I went out on deck. I could see the outline of land. Trixie was by my side. I looked at her and smiled. As usual, she seemed to read my mind and smiled back and licked my hand. She trusted me. She was telling me it's going to be okay.

My Bill seems worried. He's looking out on the water; is he praying? I can tell there's something on his mind, but I know he's going to take care of me.

By the time I got back to our room, the word going around was we were going to be docking. Oh my God. I ran up to the deck with my heart in my throat. The ship was almost at the dock. Fort Dix already? No, please, No.

The sign read, Pouch Terminal, Staten Island. Staten Island? I was home. My folks lived about two miles from here. This was unbelievable, a miracle. God was still looking over me and certainly still looking over Trixie.

My Bill keeps saying, "We're here. We're home." Another home? I'm confused, but my Bill is so happy, so this must be good.

I ran to the deck. Lower on the dock, I could see workers, lots of them, very busy unloading trucks, moving supplies, etc. A closer look revealed that all of the workers were women. With most of the men at war, women had taken on most of the jobs at docks, factories, airfields—everywhere.

My eyes scanned the crowd; I must have known someone down there. Staten Island was a very small place.

Wait a minute, that woman looks familiar. Was that Helen? I went to high school with her. Yes, it is Helen. I started yelling, "Helen, Helen, Helen."

There was too much noise down on the dock. She couldn't hear. I kept yelling. Soon, several of the soldiers and sailors around me started yelling too, "Helen, Helen, Helen."

This wasn't working. I told the guys around me, "This is my only chance. I'm going AWOL."

No one could stop me. I ran down the gangplank carrying Trixie. No one seemed to notice. The guys were still yelling, "Helen, Helen."

I ran up to her. She turned around startled, but smiled, "William? William Morris?"

"Yes, it's me. Helen, will you please do me a big favor and get Trixie to my home?"

I hugged Trixie and looked into her eyes. "I'll see you soon, girl. Be good." Then not looking back and fighting tears, I ran back to the ship.

No one even missed me.

I looked down and saw Helen cradling my dog, my best friend, my guardian angel.

I whispered to myself, "I'll see you soon, girl. I'll see you soon." I kept waving, but they had disappeared in a sea of people.

Who is this lady? She seems nice. Why is my Bill leaving? What is going on? I know he's sad to leave me. I see tears in his eyes,

but he tells me he'd see me soon. He says to be good. Why is he leaving me? The nice lady pats my head. "He'll be back, Trixie. He'll be back. Don't you worry. You'll be okay."

I feel a little better, but I miss my Bill. I have to believe I'll see him again.

Photo of William Morris Jr. and Trixie published in the Staten Island Advance as Morris was on his way to Fort Dix.

Chapter Fourteen
Reunited

I knew Trixie would be all right. A few hours later, I was officially allowed off the ship. There were buses waiting for us. I looked around. The dock was filled with people—workers, soldiers, sailors. I couldn't see Helen or Trixie, and there was no time to find a phone to call home. I had to trust she'd be fine. We boarded the buses for Fort Dix, New Jersey. Boy was I glad Trixie wasn't going there with me.

Fort Dix might as well have been called Fort Dixie.

Usually soldiers returning from war were given a heroes' welcome—parades, special dinners, free time, all the trappings due men who had risked their lives for their country—but not for us.

There was no parade. Nothing.

They barely greeted us. We were told where our barracks were—that was it. It hit me in the face like a bucket of ice water. Nothing had changed. America was just as racist as when I left it. No one cared what we'd been through. They acted as if we were invisible. Thank God we were still together, my guys, the unit. At least we had each other.

Other soldiers coming home were allowed to do nothing until their official discharge. We were given rookie assignments instead. Pick up garbage, police the area for litter, that sort of thing. This was what the army saw fit for men who'd survived

Omaha Beach, D-Day, the Battle of the Bulge, and numerous days under fire.

It dampened our spirit, but we did what we were told to do. In the end we just had to keep saying to ourselves, we're home.

Most soldiers coming back with our kind of experience were asked to re-enlist.

They barely whispered the word "re-enlistment" to our unit. Lord knows they didn't want *us* back, but a few of the guys from the unit did re-enlist. God bless them.

It was a week before I got to a phone.

I knew Norcie was at work, so I called my Mom. Susie Morris, my mother, was a no nonsense woman. Helen would have taken Trixie to my mom. I never had a dog growing up, so I couldn't imagine what was going on. The phone rang twice, and then I finally heard a familiar voice.

"Mom, it's me, Junior (that's what they called me). I'm in Fort Dix, in New Jersey. I'll be home soon. Where's Trixie?" It occurred to me that this first phone call wasn't about when I'd see her, my mother, but how was my dog? But Mom took it in stride.

"Mom, don't let Trixie around any kids. She doesn't like kids."

Even though we never had any problems, we'd trained Trixie to chase kids away from our trucks because they often messed with the gas tanks.

I heard my mother laugh, what a wonderful sound.

"Trixie has been playing with the neighborhood kids since the moment I brought her home. They love her, but she's not here." My heart stopped.

"As soon as I gave her some water and let her rest a bit, I took her to Norcie. That's where you'll find her when you get home."

Whew. What a relief. I did finally ask about my father and the rest of my family, but too soon, I had to get off the phone.

I couldn't help smiling. Trixie was safe. Trixie was home.

Helen talks to me as she drives. She tells me she went to school with my Bill. She said he was a nice man so I must be a nice dog. I liked her. As we drive along, I can see this new place is very different from camp. The houses are not all torn down and broken like in the other place; people are walking along in different kinds of clothes, not the uniforms my Bill and the guys have to wear.

It wasn't too long before we stop in front of a really big house, .a nice house with a yard and trees.

Helen carries me up the steps and knocks on the door.

A small woman comes to the door. I hear Helen tell her that Bill was coming home and this is his dog.

"This is Trixie, Mrs. Morris. Bill ran down from the ship and gave her to me; he wanted me to get her home."

The woman looks down at me, and kind of smiles.

"Thank you, Helen. I'll see she gets to his wife. Thank you."

The other woman takes me from Helen's arms. She carries me inside and puts me down. I can tell she doesn't know what to do with me.

"Are you thirsty, Trixie? I guess I can give you some water. You must be a very special dog. My son must love you very much."

Son? This was my Bill's mother.

❈

I couldn't wait to get home. It was so frustrating to be so close and not be able to go there.

Our time at Fort Dix was such a waste, but no one questions the army.

It started to dawn on the guys once we got our discharge papers that we'd probably never see each other again. We started collecting addresses; we'd been through hell, and there was no way we could forget it or each other.

Every meal now, every card game, would be the last time we would be together. Leaving the army would be bittersweet. I couldn't wait to leave, to go home, but I hated leaving the guys; they were my brothers, my family.

About a week later, we were assembled and given our discharge papers. Again, there was no fanfare, no parade, and no thanks. I packed my gear in my duffle for the last time. A group of us boarded buses outside the base. Some of us parted there, a hug, a promise of "see you soon," and a lump in our throats.

I boarded the bus and paid. Yes, we had to pay to get home, to get to a bus route where I could transfer to another bus to get me to Staten Island.

The trip home took almost three hours. I was too excited to be tired. I didn't have a chance to call before I got home; this would be a surprise for everyone, especially Trixie.

The bus let me off one block from the house where my wife, Norcie, and her sisters lived: 15 Castleton Avenue. My heart was pounding as I ran up the outside steps of the building, and then had to climb up the long stairway to the main apartment.

Before I even put the key in the lock, I heard scratching and whimpering at the door.

I've been feeling nervous all day. I don't know why. I have everything I need—and so many women to take care of me. My Bill's mother put me in her car and brought me here. She told me I was going to Bill's house. I got so excited—my Bill would be there.

But no Bill. He isn't home yet. That's what she said. Norcie is her name and she is Bill's mate, his wife. She is very pretty and so kind. And she lives here with her sisters. It's like a litter. There's Madelyn and Mamie and their cousin Bernice. They gathered around me that first day and hugged and kissed and patted me. Madelyn was the oldest, I think. They all listen to her. She is the best cook. They are all good cooks, but she gives me the best meals.

I am fine here. I have good food, these nice women, children to play with, and a yard, but today I just can't stop thinking about my Bill. I don't want to eat. I don't want to play. They think I am sick.

But then I feel him. I feel him very close. Someone is coming up the steps. I know that walk, I smell him. It's my Bill. I know it.

I opened the door, and there she was. Trixie barked and barked, ran around and around in circles, her tail wagging like crazy.

"Trixie, Trixie, I'm HOME. Where are you, girl? Trixie."

She jumped about three feet into my arms and licked my face, hand, and ears. I fell to the floor and hugged her. We rolled around and around, laughing and crying.

I didn't even realize Norcie and her sisters had come home from work. They just stood around us; they were laughing, too. We must have been quite a sight. I think they had tears in their eyes as they watched this reunion. I know I was crying with joy.

Yes, my wife was glad to see me. My family rejoiced at my safe return, but nothing could be sweeter than being reunited with my Trixie. We were together again, at last.

William A. Morris Jr. medals finally issued to him 40 years after the war. They arrived one day in his mailbox.

Chapter Fifteen
Last Days

I settled into life after war, and so did Trixie.

My family owned a moving business, Morris Moving, so I went to work for the family business.

Norcie and I moved to a large apartment above the office at 88 Barker Street. It was about a year after I got home. I wanted a normal life. I never wanted to think about the war again. And of course, I had Trixie—she was part of the family.

I really like my home. Yes, this is my home. Bill and his mate, Norcie, took me to a new house not long after my Bill and I came back from the big boat. I had so many people taking care of me.

But when we moved again to this new house, I knew I was finally home. It had a yard, actually two yards for me to play and dig in. And the men who worked with my Bill built me my own house. Sometimes when it rains and I just want to take a nap, I go to my house in the yard. My house, my own house.

I was an estimator, driver, and moved furniture in my father's business. After a while, at night I went to Wagner College, and studied commercial law.

Norcie worked too, in the city, but soon she wanted to start a family. It was time, time to get back to normal.

Trixie adjusted faster than I did.

She had the run of Morris Moving—the office, the garage, and two yards—mine and my parents (at 82 Barker Street), which was next door.

Everyone knew her. She knew the kids in the neighborhood and the men who worked at the moving company. People who never ever had a dog played with her and seemed to look forward to her visits.

My father, a big imposing man but a very gentle soul, loved when Trixie came to the office. She'd say hello to everyone: my sister Edith, who had her own desk; my sister Amy, who also had her own desk; and cousin Drudie—Drusilla Poole, who was the accountant. They all loved Trixie's visits, but after she licked hands and allowed pats, she settled next to my father and laid by him for a good long time.

Visiting the place they call the "office" is fun. Most of my Bill's family is here. Usually after my Norcie feeds me and talks to me for a while, I go out. First checking my house and then greeting the men in the garage. I walk down the driveway, keeping a safe distance from the big "moving trucks"—as my Bill calls them, make a right turn, and go into the office. Everyone there is always very busy. There are ringing sounds constantly; my Bill calls them "phones."

I greet Amy, Grandma Morris, my Bill's mother, a sweet woman called cousin Drudie, my Bill's sisters Amy and Edith, and then I go to my favorite place. My Bill's father has a little rug by his chair, and I know it is just for me. I can feel so much strength from him, and I knew my Bill loved him so much, so I do, too. I lie here on my rug by my Bill's father's leg for a long time, every day. Sometimes he reaches down and pats me while he is talking on the phone or doing his work. Whenever I look up at his face, he smiles at me.

Our life settled into normal. We had our first baby, a girl we named her Dolores. Trixie seemed to be fine with the baby. There was no jealousy. She watched over her when Dolores was in her playpen outside in the yard; she ran to tell Norcie when the baby was crying.

I talked to Trixie every day, just like we did in the war. Sometimes we played "fetch" during lunch break or before I went to school in the evening or after dinner. I could tell she was happy. She didn't wander off like she used to overseas, but she must have managed some roaming because she had many litters.

So many litters that she drove Norcie crazy, but we had no trouble finding homes for them. Everyone wanted one of Trixie's pups.

My Bill and my Norcie have a pup—a baby. Very small, she looks at me and smiles a lot. I have pups, too. So many, and my Norcie

helps me take care of them. They wander around getting into trouble, but when they are old enough, my Bill and my Norcie find wonderful people to take them. I am not sad. My Bill found me—or I found him—and look how I am loved. I know my pups will find love, too.

I came home from work one day, and Norcie couldn't wait to tell me what had happened. It seems Dolores, about three years old, had decided to wander out of the yard. Somehow she'd escaped from her playpen and started walking down the driveway—the driveway where our huge trucks come in and out all day.

Where did the baby go? Her pen is empty. I just saw her playing in there. My Norcie is in the house. Where is the baby? I sniff around, and then I see her. She is walking down the driveway, the driveway with the "moving trucks."

Oh, no you don't. Come back here, baby, come back.

She doesn't listen; these pups are so stubborn. I catch up to her and grab her by the pants and start pulling her back up the driveway.

Norcie heard Dolores yelling, "Stop it, Trixie," just as she'd come out to check on the baby.

Norcie ran down the driveway and saw Trixie pulling Dolores back up it. Norcie finished the rescue. Some of the men had witnessed what was going on. They couldn't believe it. Dolores got punished and Trixie got an extra big bone and lots of hugs.

She had saved a Morris once again.

The author, Dolores Morris, 2 years old and Trixie in the back yard at 88 Barker Street, Staten Island, NY.

I never saw any of the group from 4251st Quartermaster Truck Company again—except for Wake McMahon, who was a gun expert at our camp and kept in touch after the war. Norcie and I had one reunion with some of the guys from the 369th. We got together in Harlem one night for a great time. We didn't talk about anything bad, just good stories and the good times.

I tried not to think about the war, what I saw, did, and had to do.

I only spoke of it with Trixie.

Only she knew what had happened and what we'd been through. She helped me get through the days when the dark thoughts of war would haunt me.

When Trixie was about sixteen years old, I noticed she was moving slower every day.

I didn't want to face what this meant. I fixed up her dog-house with a blanket to make her more comfortable. She was spending more and more time there. She could see everything from there. The yards, the men working, the baby in her play pen— everything.

The men helped me build a bench next to her dog-house. I could sit there as she rested, and we talked and remembered.

My time is close. Dogs can sense this. My Bill knows something is wrong. I'm sad and tired. I don't feel like running or playing. I like it in my house on the blanket my Bill gave me. I can watch my family and friends. The men stop by to talk to me. My Bill

sits with me every day. He tells me I'm his best friend. He doesn't have to tell me. I know, and he is mine.

The day she stopped eating I knew. She stayed in her little house all day. I checked on her every two hours. I knew what was coming; she was dying.

I picked her up and cradled her in my arms on my lap. I spoke softly to her, but mostly just held her.

I am not afraid. I feel so loved. My Bill is crying. He is talking to me, saying that I will be okay and that he loves me. I know I will be okay. Then I hear him, barely heard him, whisper something he's never said to me before; he holds my head close to him and says, "Thank you Trixie. Thank you."

"I love you my Bill. Thank you."

She looked up at me with so much understanding, so much love. I don't think I imagined it; no, I think she smiled. Then she closed her eyes, and she was gone.

I felt my heart break. I couldn't let her go. I held her for a long, long time. I wasn't aware of anything around me. I wasn't sure how much time had passed.

One of the men who worked for us, a man named Adolph Harris, had been watching. I guess he'd been hovering around the whole time. He slowly came up to me and put his hand on my shoulder.

"It's time, Junior. It's time to let her go. We need to put her in the ground."

Since it was against the law to bury animals on your property, we never told anyone where we buried her.

Adolph and I found a spot in the back of my mother's yard. It was a spot where Trixie had played, buried bones, chased squirrels, and played with the kids. I wrapped her in her doghouse blanket. When I laid her in the grave, my tears wet the blanket and the dirt around it. I sobbed like a baby. I think that was the saddest day of any day I'd lived. It all came back to me: the war, the D-Day battles, the Battle of the Bulge, the soldier pushing the gun into my face. None of that wore on my heart as heavy as losing this dog. I would be dead if it were not for her. She kept me safe; she was sent from God to protect me. I truly believe that. I had lost my best friend.

Finally, I walked away and left Adolph to finish.

For many years, I visited the spot. I still spoke to her, told her what was going on. I felt she was there. I always ended our talks the same way.

"Love you, Trixie. Love you, girl. Thank you."

Love you my Bill. Thank you.

The End.

MOURNING the loss of an old friend — his dog, Trixie — is Bill Morris Jr., West Brighton moving man. Trixie came home with Bill from the war in Europe in 1945, sporting a combat record as impressive as Bill's. At that time a sergeant in a truck outfit, Bill picked up the pup, "a sort of terrier," in England's Southampton. Trixie went over with Bill on the D-Day invasion of Normandy, and was at his side through the war in Europe, right into Czechoslovakia. Trixie picked up an "honorary Purple Heart" in Germany when shrapnel hit her in the legs, and later won a citation from the regimental commander after spotting and running in to attack three German soldiers who were hiding for a roadside ambush. Old age caught up with her the other day.

Trixie's obituary which Morris carries in his wallet to this day.

About the Author

Dolores N. Morris is a sixth generation Staten Island native. She is widely recognized for her work in television at such prestigious companies as Children's Television Workshop, ABC Television, Walt Disney Television and HBO.

Her career has spanned 30 years of producing award winning family and children's programming, resulting in 3 Peabody Awards, an Oscar mention and 5 Emmy awards.

Dolores serves on several community boards and is also a motivational speaker, targeting the empowerment of women and underserved youth.

She is a certified Lay Speaker of the United Methodist church and recipient of awards such as the National Council of Negro Women, The College of Staten Island Presidents Medal, Lambda Kappa Mu, The Staten Island branch of the NAACP Humanitarian Award and was installed in the first class of Port Richmond High School, her alma mater's, Hall of Fame.

Dolores and her siblings, Joan and William III, formed a Christian singing group, Faith Music Ministry that performs throughout the New York area.

She lives her life believing in the adage she once heard her grandfather, William A Morris Sr., say. "If you want something done and done well, ask a busy person."

35716879R00068

Made in the USA
Middletown, DE
12 October 2016